Susan Conolly Horne has been secretly writing children's stories for years! She grew up in Athens, Georgia, but raised her family in a town not too far from Athens called Decatur.

Susan became a teacher of young children and lucky for her, she learned how important reading and writing are. Many of her ideas have been shaped by the people and events around her. She loves teaching young children and adults and is now retired and lives in Covington, Georgia. She devotes much of her time to creating and continuing to write her own stories.

SUSAN CONOLLY HORNE

THE OLD-FASHIONED WAY

AUSTIN MACAULEY PUBLISHERS™
LONDON • CAMBRIDGE • NEW YORK • SHARJAH

Copyright © Susan Conolly Horne (2020)

Ordering Information:
Quantity sales: special discounts are available on quantity purchases by corporations, associations, and others. For details, contact the publisher at the address below.

Publisher's Cataloging-in-Publication data
Conolly Horne, Susan
The Old-Fashioned Way

ISBN 9781647501792 (Paperback)
ISBN 9781647501785 (Hardback)
ISBN 9781647501808 (ePub e-book)

Library of Congress Control Number: 2020913245

www.austinmacauley.com/us

First Published (2020)
Austin Macauley Publishers LLC
40 Wall Street, 28th Floor
New York, NY 10005
USA

mail-usa@austinmacauley.com
+1 (646) 5125767

Lianne and Emma, who always believe and encourage me to follow my dreams.

I am grateful to my sisters Cathy and Jane, who took the time to read, edit, and discuss my book in a way that was honest, respectful, and encouraging.

For Emma, first grade was a scary place. Everything felt really big—her classroom, the library, the playground. And she didn't know many people there. You see, it was hard for Emma to make friends. Then one day, out of the blue, Emma met Molly. It seemed like they became friends instantly!

THE OLD-
FASHIONED
WAY

Molly always played with Emma outside and sat with her at lunch. Emma and Molly loved seeing what they had in their lunchboxes. Sometimes they would trade with each other and sometimes at the end of the day they walked home together. Soon they became the best of friends!

One day Emma came home from school and told her Mia that she wanted to do something special for her friend Molly.

"Mia, what can I do?"

"Well," Mia said, "think about what Molly likes."

Emma began to think. "I know! Molly loves cookies! Let's go to the store and buy cookies!"

Mia thought about this and said, "That would be very nice Emma, but why don't we do it the old-fashioned way and bake our own?"

THE OLD-FASHIONED WAY

Emma asked, "What do you mean *the old-fashioned way?* Buying cookies at the store is fast and they taste good."

Mia replied, "That's true Emma, but when you take the time to bake Molly cookies, this becomes a gift from the heart and not just a gift from a store. You see, the more you put into a gift the happier it is to give to someone. A long time ago people used to make gifts all the time and now this way has become *the old-fashioned way.* Why don't we try it and see how it feels?"

Emma and her Mia searched for a special cookie recipe that Molly would love. Emma said, "Let's go to the computer and find a recipe. It will take no time at all!" Just as Emma said these words, Mia was pulling down an old recipe book that always lived on the shelf and had belonged to Emma's grandmother.

The book was not a new book, in fact it looked old and tattered. The paper was thin and spotted as if someone had dropped something on the pages. Emma said, "Mia, why look there? This book looks old and messy. Some of the pages are even falling out!"

THE OLD-
FASHIONED
WAY

Mia held the book close to her heart and said, "The words on these pages are like treasures passed down again and again from different people in our family. These recipes are like threads from the past that help connect us to the future. Cooking from this book is the old-fashioned way.

THE OLD-
FASHIONED
WAY

Mmm, look! Here is a Cranberry Chocolate Chip cookie recipe that I bet Molly would love. Shall we try it?"

cranberry chocolate chip
cookie recipe

So that afternoon Emma and her Mia baked Cranberry Chocolate Chip Cookies from the old, battered family recipe book. The whole kitchen – in fact, the whole house—smelled like a warm, melting piece of chocolate.

THE OLD-
FASHIONED
WAY

2 cups all-purpose flour
1 cup old fashioned rolled oats
1 teaspoon baking powder
1 teaspoon baking soda
1 teaspoon salt
2½ sticks butter at room temperature
1 cup brown sugar
½ cup granulated sugar
1 large egg and 1 egg yolk at room temperature
1 teaspoon vanilla
1½ cups semisweet chocolate chips
1½ cups dried cranberries

Preheat oven 325°F
First, mix together flour, oats, baking powder, baking soda and salt.
Next, in a separate bowl, mix vanilla, butter, both sugars, and the egg and egg yolk until creamy.
Last of all, mix the dry ingredients with the wet ingredients and add chocolate chips and cranberries.
Drop dough on baking sheet 2 inches apart using a spoon. Bake until edges of cookies are brown.
(5 to 10 minutes) Let cool before eating.

THE OLD-
FASHIONED
WAY

cranberry chocolate chip
cookie recipe

8 oz unsalted butter,softened
1 1/2 cup dark brown sugar
2 large eggs
2 teaspoon pure vanilla extract
         purpose flour
    on baking soda
    oon sea salt
    oon baking powder
    ried cranberries
    chocolate chips

1. pre-heat oven to 350 f.line 2 baking
paper and set aside
2.in a large mixer,combine the softened but
sugar with a whisk attachment.let whisk for 2
eggs one at a time,followed by the vanilla extra
baking soda,sea salt and baking powder and s
making sure not to over-mix batter.

While the cookies cooled, Mia pulled out some wrapping paper and friendship cards for Emma to use to wrap the cookies. Emma took one look and ran to get her art box.

Mia said, "Emma you don't have to do that. I have some wrapping paper you can use to wrap these cookies. Emma said, "No thank you, Mia. This gift has come straight from my heart and I want to do the wrapping the *old-fashioned way!*"

THE OLD-
FASHIONED
WAY

28

CPSIA information can be obtained
at www.ICGtesting.com
Printed in the USA
LVHW070853230920
666824LV00004B/295